AMERICAN ELVES - THE YANKOOS

THE YANKOOS

AND

THE OAK-HICKORY FOREST ECOLOGY

BOOK FIVE

By Robert Frieders, Ph.D.

One of a Yankoo Series of Books

COVER: Lucky, the Yankoo reporter, stands outside his hut. Lying there on the ground is a Deer skull with horns on it. He is examining it. He has studied the habits of the forest Whitetail Deer. His research on deer will be published in the Yankoo Gazette.

Yankoo Publishing Co.

AMERICAN ELVES - THE YANKOOS

THE YANKOOS

AND

THE OAK-HICKORY FOREST ECOLOGY

BOOK FIVE

By Robert Frieders, Ph.D.

All photographs and line drawings by the author, except the deer photos on pages 6,7,8,9,14: Courtesy of John T. Kruer

Published by: The Yankoo Publishing Co.
10616 W. Cameo Drive
Sun City, AZ 85351-2708

First Printing l997

Printed in the United States of America

Library of Congress Catalog Card Number 93-61530

ISBN 0-9639284-5-7

Acknowledgments

Dottie, our computer editor, and I wish to thank our friends who have helped us make this book a reality.

Our Consultant - Dr. Mamie Ross
Our Editor - Professor Marge Edwards

We are all proud of this book on the plant and animal life of the Oak-Hickory Forest. It is our hope that each of you will consider yourself to be the "Friend" as you read this book. May the American Elves, the Yankoos, provide you with an interesting adventure as you learn about life in the forest.

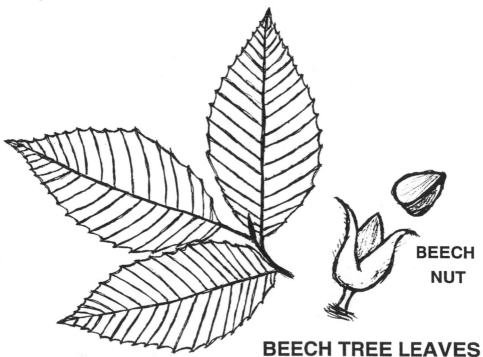

BEECH NUT

BEECH TREE LEAVES

Table of Contents

WILD GRAPE

CHAPTER ONE
LUCKY - THE YANKOO REPORTER

Glad to see you again, my friend. Come with me. We shall deliver the Yankoo mail together. Up ahead is Lucky's hut. He is our Yankoo reporter. He is looking at a deer skull with antlers on it. Hi, Lucky. Hi, Lester. What do you think about this buck? It was a big one. I am doing a story on the Whitetail Deer. It will be in the Yankoo Gazette.

Look at this picture. That is a male deer, a buck. It is hiding there among those small trees. Let me tell you about the Whitetail Deer.

All of these deer have white tails. That tail is very important to the deer. Deer signal information with that tail. If the tail wags from side to side, the signal indicates "everything is all right". If that tail stops wagging, that is the "be alert" signal. Then, if the tail is raised high, that means "flee". Off go all the deer! As they run away, one sees the white underside of that tail. It is raised high over the back of every deer.

If you observe the deer, you can learn these signals.

These deer can travel fast. In short spurts, they can go about forty miles per hour. They can jump over obstacles in their way. They can leap over things some eight feet high.

The Whitetail Deer are active at dawn and dusk. During those times, they secure food. Deer are browsers. They eat leaves, twigs,grasses, fruits, nuts,

and lichens, like these on this rock. While eating, they chew food fast. They eat large amounts of food very quickly. Then, a deer retires to some protected area. There, it rests and "chews the cud".

Let me tell you about that.

A deer's stomach has four chambers. The food it eats quickly goes to the first chamber, then, to the second chamber. There, it is broken down into small rounded masses called cud. While resting, a small amount of cud is brought back to the mouth cavity. It has never been really chewed. Now, it is really chewed. Then, it is sent down to the third and fourth stomach chambers to be digested. While resting, the deer "chews its cud".

A deer's eyesight is not too keen. However, it can pick up faint sounds. Faint odors in the wind are also easily detected, so a deer is adequately warned of danger.

Only male deer, the bucks, have horns. These horns are called antlers. A buck makes new antlers every year. Every year, it sheds these antlers. Let's say we have a young buck. It is making its first antlers. Growth of antlers starts in April or May. Bumps of skin appear on each side of the forehead. This skin is covered by soft hair. One says the buck is "in velvet". Inside this skin growth, a bone is being formed. Eventually, it will reach mature size. It will be firmly attached to the front bone of the skull.

For this buck, the antlers are a single spike on each side. This is called a brow tine antler. It forms on the brow. A tine is a point on an antler. The brow antlers have one point each. These antlers will be fully grown in August or September. Up until that time, the deer is "in velvet".

Once the antlers are fully grown, blood vessels at the base close off. Now, the skin covering the antlers dies. The skin dries up. The deer now tries to rub off the dried skin on the antlers. It rubs the antlers against tree trunks. It also rubs against branches of small trees. This will clear off all dried skin.

Later in the year, this buck will shed its brow tine antlers. Every year, a buck makes new antlers. Every year, the antlers will be larger. Every year, there will be more points, more tines to the antlers. The kind and amount of food eaten have an effect on the antler size. Here, I have made a drawing showing, year by year, how antlers grow.

First year   Second year

Third year   Fourth year

In October, the buck stakes out its territory. Large scent glands develop on either side of its forehead. The buck rubs these glands against tree trunks. Liquid scent will be forced out of the gland. It will stick to the tree bark. Trees all around the territory will be marked with this buck scent. It indicates to other bucks that this area is taken. The buck will defend this area with its antlers.

The rutting season now begins. It extends from October to January. The buck sets about attracting does to his territory. The buck will mate with a number of does. These does will stay with the buck. The buck will defend these does.

In January, the rutting season ends. This group setup now breaks down. Does and bucks will now live separately. The antlers are no longer needed to defend the does and the territory. Then, the antlers are shed. The antler attachment to the front skull bone is weakened. Often, the antlers drop off. To hasten the process, the bucks push the antlers against a tree trunk. This will break the weakened antler attachment to the skull. The antlers will be shed. The skull area where antlers were attached will be covered over.

"Bachelor" group of Bucks

Now, the deer sexes live separately. Bucks form "bachelor" groups. About two to five bucks form a band. During this time, they will live together.

Bucks, by nature, are very aggressive. One buck will try to dominate another buck. Weaker bucks accept stronger bucks without a contest.

Often, however, these groups have several bucks that appear equally strong. Then, a contest is needed to establish the dominant buck. In such a contest, the following happens.

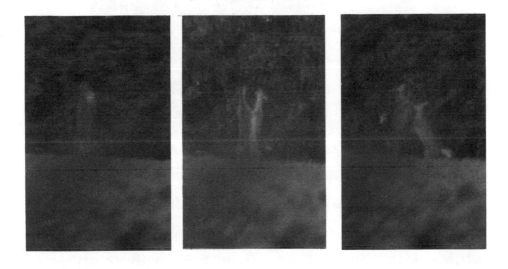

Each buck rises up on his hind feet near the other. With front feet high in the air, each buck strikes at the other. Eventually, the stronger buck prevails. The other buck backs off. So, in the "bachelor" groups, there is a dominance established among all the bucks in the group.

The does, in the meantime, have formed female groups. Does that have their first birth will only have a single fawn.

In subsequent years, this doe will always have twins or triplets. In May or June, each doe will live alone with the fawns. Yearlings usually spend the first winter with the mother. Fawns lose their spots in about four months. By fall, the fawns will be almost as large as their mother.

That, my friend, is the life cycle of our deer. This research will be published in the Yankoo Gazette. That is our Yankoo paper. Well, I must be off to work on a report on our forest ferns. Glad to have met you, my friend. Goodbye, Lester. Goodbye, Lucky.

CHAPTER TWO

LESTER - ON HIS MAIL ROUTE

Lester walks past a male Cardinal bird. Cardinals are found along the edges and in open spaces of the forest. Their favorite nesting spots are dense bushes and thickets.

Look at that Wheel Bug. It is rightly named. Notice it has what looks like a wheel on its back. This Wheel Bug is also an assassin. It lies in wait at flowers. There, it will capture and kill insects. It has captured and eaten many a Honey Bee. It also searches out caterpillars eating tree leaves. The Wheel Bug can give one a good bite. But it is not like the rest of the assassin bug family. In other parts of the world, assassin bugs are blood suckers. They suck blood from animals.

Oh, look over there. That is one of our spring flowers. It is flowering. See how it grows through the forest leaves. That plant is called Dutchman's Breeches. Look closely at those flowers. Notice each flower looks like a baggy pair of pants. That plant has been named after the shape of the flowers. Each flower hangs by its legs from the flower stem. I often see bumblebees visiting the flowers. Their long tongues can reach the pools of nectar deep in those flowers.

It's Dogwood time in our forest. Notice how many trees are blooming now. In the spring, the large white flowers brighten up our forest. Most kinds of trees, my friend, first produce leaves in the spring. Later, these trees produce the flowers. The Dogwood tree is different. It produces the flowers first, then the leaves.

Dogwood trees produce two kinds of winter buds. One kind is long and pointed at the end. In the spring, it will make the new stem and leaves. The other kind is rounded and on a stalk. In the spring, this bud will make a flower.

Winter Flower Bud   Winter Stem and Leaves Bud

How many flowers will a Dogwood tree have next spring? That's an easy question to answer. In the fall or winter, count the flower buds on the tree. You will know exactly how many flowers that tree will have in the spring.

Here is a picture of a Dogwood tree. It has many, many winter flower buds. It will have many flowers in the spring.

Here is a picture I took last spring. On the right is a winter bud of the Beech tree. Notice the bud is covered by brown scales. They protect the delicate structures inside. Underneath the scales is a woolly layer. This keeps the bud from drying out. It also protects it from cold winter temperatures. A very miniature stem and leaves are inside the woolly layer. This bud was made in midsummer. It will stay at this stage during the fall and winter. Then come spring and warm weather. Now, the bud structures inside grow rapidly. The covering bud scales are forced aside. The undeveloped stem starts to lengthen quickly. The miniature folded leaves start to unfold and grow in size. That is what the picture on the left shows. Notice the leaves are still folded somewhat. They will unfold entirely and grow to mature size. Then, growth stops. All this takes place within a few days. This happens with all the buds on the Beech tree at the same time. Within a short time, the Beech tree is once again covered with leaves.

Look over there, my friend.   See the bird on that tree. It is a male Belted Kingfisher.   That is one of the bird's favorite perching spots. I often see it there as

I deliver the mail. The Kingfishers have a nest in the bank of a nearby stream. They dug out a tunnel in the rather steep clay bank. They have an enlarged nesting area at the end of that tunnel. Ichabod, the Yankoo fisherman, told me about those birds. He fishes nearby in the stream. He has seen the birds capture small fish and crayfish. He says they also like insects.

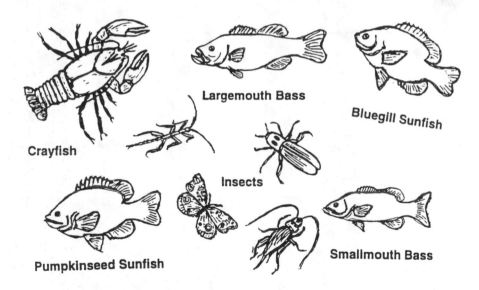

Largemouth Bass

Bluegill Sunfish

Crayfish

Insects

Pumpkinseed Sunfish

Smallmouth Bass

Oh, there goes the Kingfisher. It continues to patrol the area looking for food.

This part of our forest is rather wet. There are some springs in the area. Many interesting animals live in these moist parts of our forest.

One day, I spent some time here watching a land snail. Let's see if we can spot one.

Yes, here is one. Notice how it moves along on that white foot. As it moves, it pours out a sticky slime on the ground. The snail moves easily over this slime cover. Two long tentacles come off the head end. At the end of each tentacle is an eye. If I put my hand near it, see what happens.   Both tentacles disappeared into the head area. There, out come those tentacles with the eyes. Snails have teeth. They eat green plants.

They don't bite off bits of food. No, snails have a unique structure - a scraper. In the mouth area, the snail has a belt-like structure. Embedded in this belt are rows of small teeth. Here is a drawing of a belt.

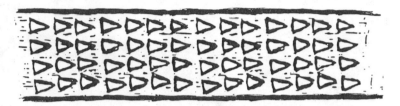

This belt-like structure is called radula by scientists. The word radula means scraper in the Latin language. That is a good name. It is a real scraper. Here are some drawings I made. They show how this scraper works.

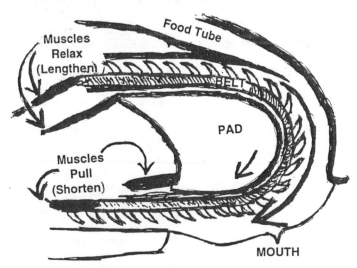

The belt with the teeth moves over a pad. The belt is pulled into position for eating.

Muscles at one end pull the belt and the pad downward. Arrows indicate this movement.

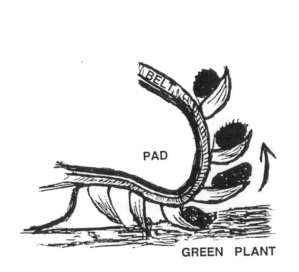

PAD

GREEN PLANT

The mouth opens. The pad pushes the teeth against the green plant. Then, muscles at the other end of the belt b e g i n t o shorten.

This pulls the belt back upwards. Arrows indicate this action. As the belt moves upwards, the teeth dig into the plant and scrape off bits of the plant. The belt moves upwards with these bits of plant material.

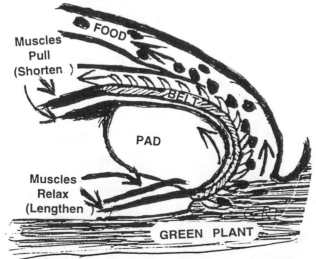

Muscles
Pull
(Shorten)

FOOD

BELT

PAD

Muscles
Relax
(Lengthen)

GREEN PLANT

Into the food tube, these plant pieces go. They will be digested in the snail's stomach.

The end of the belt is reached. Then, the belt is quickly brought back downwards again. It will scrape off more plant food. So as the snail moves, the scraper goes up and down. The snail is eating more and more food. This scraper is an ideal food-getter for the snail.

How many rows of teeth are there? Well, that varies with different kinds of snails. So does the shape of the teeth. The teeth are very small. As the teeth wear out, they are replaced with new teeth.

That is quite a unique way of securing food, don't you think? During the hot summer months, these snails rest. They seal themselves off in their shells. A snail moves back entirely into the shell. Then, it secretes a slimy material that dries and closes off the opening.

When the hot weather passes, the snail cuts away this covering.Once more, it seeks plants to scrape for food.

CHAPTER THREE
JASPER - THE YANKOO SCHOOLMASTER

Up ahead is our Yankoo schoolmaster, Jasper. He
has studied our forest Bumblebees. Hi, Jasper. My
friend would enjoy learning about Bumblebees. Hi,
Lester. I'd be happy to tell him about the forest
Bumblebees. We have a colony near by.

Look over there, my friend. Several Bumblebees are by that rock. One just disappeared under that rock. One just came out from under that rock. It just flew away.

My friend, we have here an underground Bumblebee nest. Let me tell you about these Bumblebees. Their life cycle is quite different from the Honey Bee. You know, Honey Bees live in hives. They store honey in the hives. When cold weather comes, they stay inside the hive. It is warm there, and they have much honey food. When spring comes, out come the Honey Bees. Back to work again!

It doesn't happen that way with Bumblebees. Things are different with Bumblebees.

In the fall, new male and queen Bumblebees are produced. The males then fertilize the new queen Bumblebees. Shortly after this, the males die. The newly-fertilized queen Bumblebees now leave the nest. Then, all the worker Bumblebees in the nest die.

As winter approaches, only the newly-fertilized queen Bumblebees are alive. All the rest of the Bumblebees have died. In the spring, each queen will start a new Bumblebee colony.

The new queens must find a place to spend the winter. An abandoned, underground mouse's nest is often selected.

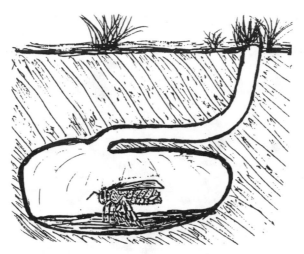

The queen sets about securing food for the winter stay underground. First, it makes a honey pot. Here is a drawing showing how it is made. Bumblebees have wax glands between their abdomen plates.

These glands secrete wax scales. The queen pulls off these scales with its legs. Then, with its mouth and feet, it fashions a honey pot.

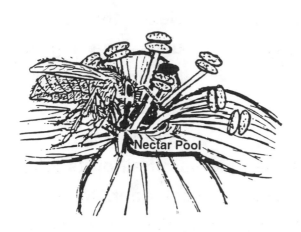

After the pot is made, the queen seeks out fall flowers. It pushes the end of its long tongue into the flowers' nectar pools.

Using its tongue as a straw, the queen bee sucks up the nectar. The nectar goes into a special nectar crop.

While gathering this nectar, the Bumblebee brushes up against the pollen-bearing parts of the flower. The sticky pollen grains adhere to the hairy legs of the Bumblebee.

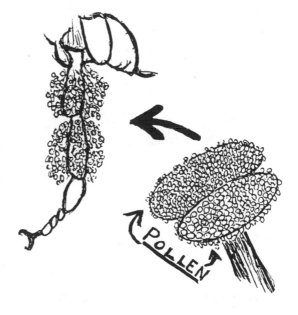

Then, off the queen bee goes to the nest. It now empties the nectar from the crop into the honey pot .

Scraping Pollen off Hairy Legs

Next, the queen uses one leg to brush the pollen grains from another leg. It brushes all the pollen grains off all of its legs. The pollen makes a pile on the nest floor. Now, the queen is ready for the winter weather. Provisions have been stored in its nest.

Given a warm spring day, the queen emerges from the nest. It finds some spring flowers. It gets nectar and pollen from these flowers. The nectar provides energy for the queen. The pollen provides the queen with protein. This protein food will be used in making eggs. Then, the queen fills up the honey pot in the nest with nectar. Pollen is collected and stored in the nest.

Next, the queen uses wax to fence in an area of the nest. This wax enclosure is called a cell. Pollen is

then formed into balls. These balls are placed in the cell. Finally, the queen lays about a dozen eggs on the pollen. Then, she broods the eggs. She stands right above the cell. Her body heat keeps the eggs warm. The eggs hatch. The larvae look like small

worms.They grow bigger, when they are fed pollen and nectar. The queen enlarges the cell as needed.

As the larvae mature, the queen encloses each one inside a new wax cell.

The mature larva now spins a white silk cocoon inside the cell. Inside this cocoon, the larva changes into a Bumblebee. Meanwhile, the queen has laid a second batch of eggs.

The first batch now emerges from their cocoons. These new Bumblebees are all females. All of these females are smaller than the queen Bumblebee. These will be the workers in the nest. Being females, they might lay a few eggs. The queen will immediately eat these eggs.

The female workers now recycle their old wax cocoon cells. They put wax rims around the top of each cell.

Some of these cells will now be used to store nectar. Other cells will be used to store pollen.

The female workers also brood and feed the larvae. From the egg stage to an adult stage takes about sixteen to twenty-five days. The Bumblebee colony grows and grows. The queen lays more and more eggs as more workers hatch from their cocoons. The workers do all the work; the queen lays the eggs.

Late in the summer, the queen produces eggs that hatch into queens or males. No more female workers are produced. That is the life cycle of Bumblebees. They are Important in our forest. They pollinate many flowers in our forest. They serve as food for some animals. The skunks love the Bumblebees. If they discover a nest, they will open it up and eat the Bumblebees. The weather of our temperate forest is ideal for Bumblebees.   Well, let's be on our mail route again, my friend. Goodbye, Jasper. Have a good day.

My friend, we should be able to find a salamander along our route. We will have to look. They are night animals. During the day, they will hide. I have found some hiding under logs, rocks, and even wet leaves.

Here is one, my friend.   That is the Redback Salamander. Notice the straight red stripe on its back. It runs from the back of the head to the tail. That is the most common kind of salamander in our forest. At night, salamanders are very active. They search the ground for insects. They even climb the plants of the area looking for food. When cold weather comes, they dig out a space underground. They spend the winter sleeping in this warm underground space.

Look at that Strawberry plant, my friend. Notice that it has two leaves on slender leaf stalks. Each leaf is divided into three leaflets. Two white flowers are blooming, now. The plant produces many flowers. Every day for several weeks, it will have flowers. The flowers succeed one another in blooming. Insects will pollinate these flowers. Each pollinated flower will then develop into a strawberry. Notice those large green structures on that plant. They are bending toward the ground. They are heavy. They were pollinated flowers. Now, they are developing into strawberries.

In spring and early summer, our forest has many, many insects. Many forest animals depend on these insects for food. From mid-summer into fall, the insects become fewer in numbers. The forest now provides Huckleberries, Blueberries, and Strawberries. Animals have a new food source - the berries. The Strawberry plant will advertise its fruit.

A hungry animal can't miss its bright red color. The animal eats the strawberry. For this food, it will deposit strawberry seeds in a new spot. Its droppings will contain many strawberry seeds. With fertilizer at hand, a seed will probably develop into a new strawberry plant. My friend, plants and animals depend upon one another.

Look, my friend. There is something I don't see every day. See those ducks along the side of the brook. Those are Mallard ducks. The ducklings are busy eating the seeds on the ground.

Oh, oh, the ducks have seen us coming! They will all go into the water and swim away.

The male and female ducks were watching their young. They stand by to protect them.

Those ducklings are expert swimmers.   Those young ducks were born with a swimming ability. See how the young all line up behind the female.

Even on land, the young ducks usually stay near the female. See how they huddle close to the female.

The male Mallard duck often trails slightly behind the family. It guards them from a distance.

Well, sometimes it stops momentarily for a bite to eat!

Look over here on this tree, my friend. That is a Pandora Sphinx Moth.

All Sphinx Moths are swift flyers. Notice the long pointed front wings of that moth. Those wings were made for speed. The hind wings are much smaller. Sphinx Moths also have a tapered body. Notice that the Pandora Sphinx has a stout body. It is tapered toward the rear. That is another characteristic feature of fast flyers.

All Sphinx Moths have relatively large eyes. This is to be expected. All animals that move about at night have proportionately larger eyes than the daytime animals. This moth is active at dusk and at night. It inserts its hollow proboscis into deep flower nectar pools. It then draws up, by suction, the nectar through this proboscis tube. The female Pandora Sphinx lays its eggs on the Grape vine leaves. I have also found them on the leaves of the Virginia Creeper vine. The Pandora Sphinx is a common forest moth.

CHAPTER FOUR

LESTER - ON HIS MAIL ROUTE

Look at that Opossum up ahead, my friend. It is daytime; yet, that Opossum is still looking for food. It is really a forest night animal. It should be sleeping. It does look dangerous, doesn't it?

Look at those sharp teeth. It is hissing at us. Now, if we tried to attack, it would probably "play Possum". It would fall down on its side. It would draw back its lips, exposing its teeth. It would close its eyes and not move. It would look like it was dead!

The Opossum does this when attacked by another animal. Most animals would probably just sniff around it. Then, they would leave. Soon, the Opossum would open its eyes. It would check to see if the coast was clear. If it was, the Opossum would rise up and scramble away.

Opossums have a pouch for their young. The babies are very, very helpless when they are born. The female licks a pathway through its fur. The new babies can now find their way to the pouch. Once in the pouch, the babies drink milk and sleep for some weeks. When they grow larger,the youngsters get out and play. Then, back into the pouch, they go. Normally, the young spend two months in the pouch. When they get too big for the pouch, they hang onto the back of the female. During the next forty days, the young stay near the adult.

Opossums are great climbers. Notice the tail. It has no hairs on it. That is a prehensile tail. They can grab things with that tail. The Opossums use it as a fifth hand. They often hang by their tail.

The Opossums, like some monkeys and apes, have an opposable thumb. We have an opposable thumb, my friend. Our thumb is separated, more or less, from the other digits. It can go up against the other digits. This allows one to grasp things. This is very useful in climbing. The Opossums can grasp the limb better with such a thumb setup. Opossums spend the

winter months sleeping in a burrow. They wake up now and then and move about in their den.

Now, we are coming to some Blackberry bushes. Plants, my friend, produce seeds. Most plants cannot scatter their seeds. This is the case with a Blackberry bush. Yet, the seed must be dispersed in the forest. To make sure the seeds are scattered, the plant produces berries. The berries have many small seeds inside. Animals eat these berries. The seeds pass undamaged through the animal. They will be cast out in the animal droppings. Some of these seeds will sprout. They will produce Blackberry plants in new forest areas. The animals have scattered the seeds for the Blackberry plant. In return, the Blackberry plant gave them some food, the Blackberries.

To make this work, the plant must produce tasty berries. The Blackberry plant "advertises" its berries.

Here is a picture of a plant with berries. Notice all those different colored d e v e l o p i n g blackberries. Some are green, some white, some slightly red, some deep red; and some are black. Animals see all those colored, developing berries. The plant is advertising - "this many berries will be produced".

So, animals know many berries will be made by this bush.

Animals now know how <u>many</u> berries will be made. If that was the only message, all the berries would be colored alike. Why does the plant use so many different colors? The Blackberry plant is signaling with different colors <u>when</u> the berries will be ripe. The plant is telling animals <u>when</u> the berries will ripen over a time span. Those black in color are mature; eat them now. The deep-red-colored berries will mature in several days. The slightly-red berries will take longer to ripen, say a week or so. Those green and white berries will take even more time to mature. They will mature in several weeks.

This information is very helpful to animals. If there is no sign of future food in an area, birds, especially, will leave. They will move to another area where there is food. Signaling that more berries will be produced is very important. The turkeys, foxes, raccoons, and White-footed Mice, especially, eat blackberries. Knowing that berries will be produced for some time helps. They will regularly check this plant.

Up ahead, see those handsome sparrows on the ground. They are eating seeds. Those are two White-crowned Sparrows. They do not stay with us all year. They migrate south to warmer areas in the winter. When the warm spring weather comes, we hear them in our forest again. One hears the male bird singing. Each male sets up a territory. It stakes out a woodland area, as it were. The area selected will have enough food for a pair of sparrows and their young. The male sings to let other males know - "This food is taken, stay away or I will drive you away."

After mating, the pair of White-crowned Sparrows sets about raising their young. They eat seeds in the territory. They also feed on flies and mosquitoes, as well as fruits and berries. I saw a sparrow sitting on a Grape vine one day. Suddenly, it sprang several feet into the air. It turned around quickly and returned to that same spot on the Grape vine. It had caught a gnat or a small flying insect. From its observation post, it can easily spot food flying by. There go those birds to another part of their territory.

As you see, many low growing plants appear above the leaves here. Those plants are Club Moss.

A common name for this Club Moss is Ground Cedar. The Ground Cedar makes a very long stem.

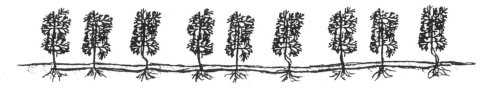

Each stem is about a yard long. This stem runs parallel to the ground. The stem sends up erect stems. These are three to four inches high. Those are the ones we see coming through the leaf layer.

Look at that Red Milk Snake going through the Ground Cedar. It moves fast. Now, it is gone.

The Red Milk Snake hid under those Ground Cedar plants and leaves. We have a number of Milk Snakes in our forest. Snakes do not brood their eggs as birds do. No, they place their eggs in a warm spot. Then, the female snake goes away. The heat will brood the eggs. The young, once hatched, fend for themselves. I took a picture of some eggs of a Milk Snake recently.

Snakes' eggs are oblong in shape. Birds' eggs are somewhat rounded. Birds' eggs have a rigid shell. Snakes' eggs give a little when they are touched. They are leathery. These eggs were under a pile of rotting grass. The heat from the rotting grass incubated the eggs. I checked these eggs often.

I wanted to see the snake's egg hatch. I was lucky. One day, I found some eggs had hatched. Here is a picture of a newly-hatched Milk Snake which came from one of those eggs.

Here is another picture from the same nest. The Milk Snake has just emerged from the egg.

Look up ahead, my friend. That is our Spotted Skunk.
It should be in its burrow sleeping. One seldom sees
it during the day. We are lucky to see it.

Notice that it has jet black fur. There is one white
spot on the forehead. The end of the tail is white.
That is a very conspicuous coloration for an animal.
There is no doubt that an animal is present. In the
case of this skunk, the coloration says, "Here I am--be
careful!"   Threatening a skunk produces major
problems for an animal.

If threatened, the skunk turns its hind end toward the animal. Straight up in the air goes the tail. This usually scares an animal away.

If it stays, the animal will regret it. That skunk glances back toward the animal. Then, it rises up on its forelegs. This raises the hindquarters high in the air.

The scent gland openings are pointed toward the "problem". Muscles suddenly squeeze those scent glands. This shoots the liquid out into the face of the animal. The skunk can shoot this liquid for ten feet.

The animal receiving the skunk's scent treatment will leave in a hurry. Never again will it bother a skunk. However, this doesn't work with owls and hawks. They hunt skunks. They don't mind the foul smelling liquid. A skunk meal is worth it to them. In the forest, the skunk does leave an odor trail. I can always tell when one is nearby. Yet, skunks have a keen sense of smell. They can pick up faint odors. These odors lead them to food. They can detect mice in their underground nests. The claws on their strong forefeet will dig them out. Mice, rats, insects, bird eggs, young birds, and wild grapes are all skunk food.

Our Spotted Skunk stays all winter. It sleeps in its burrow. Its burrow is often an abandoned one made by another animal. It can use the claws on its strong front legs to dig its own, if necessary. The skunk does not hibernate. Every now and then, the skunk gets up and wanders around a bit.

CHAPTER FIVE

JOSHUA - THE YANKOO DOCTOR

Look over there, my friend. That is Joshua, the Yankoo Doctor. Hi, Joshua. Well, hi, Lester. I didn't expect to see you.

What are you doing here, Joshua? Well, Lester, I am waiting to see what happens. I am observing a female Scarab Beetle. Scarab Beetles are some of the largest beetles in the world. Male beetles all have ferocious looking horns.

Look over there on that rotting wood. That large beetle is a Scarab Beetle. It is the largest beetle in our forest. It is called the Hercules Beetle. Some call this beetle the Unicorn Beetle. That beetle is a female beetle. It has no horns. The adult male has horns.

Here is a drawing I made of a male Hercules Beetle. Those are ferocious looking horns, aren't they?

The female beetle lays eggs on rotting wood. The eggs hatch, and the larvae eat wood. When mature, the larvae change into adult beetles.

Scarab Beetles in the tropics use the horns at mating time. The female beetles give off a scent that attracts male beetles. That female has probably given its mating scent. If it has, there will soon be male beetles coming. The males then engage in combat to win the female. Those male horns do not injure another male. No, the horns are used to lift another male off the ground. Then, it turns the male over on its back.

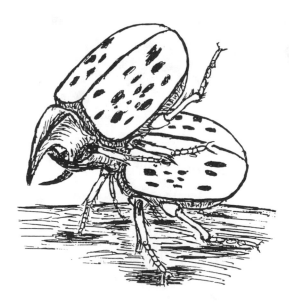

I am waiting for the males to come. I want to see two males in combat. Well, Joshua, I hope those males come and fight. My friend and I must go on delivering mail. Goodbye, Joshua. Goodbye, Lester.

Look at that Oak Apple on the ground there, my friend. It looks like a brown apple, doesn't it?

Animals and plants in our forest help each other in many interesting ways. Animals depend upon plants. Plants depend upon animals. This gall was made by an oak leaf. It did this at the request of a very small wasp. Let me explain how this very interesting setup occurs.

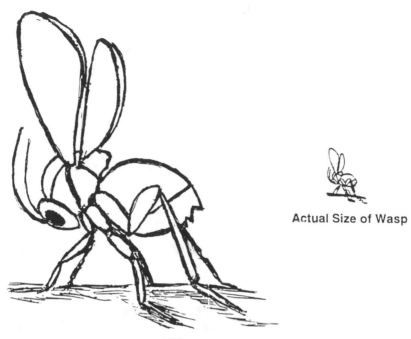

Actual Size of Wasp

Enlarged drawing of Wasp

Here is a drawing of the wasp involved. As you can see, it is very, very small. The female wasp lays eggs on the oak leaf. The eggs hatch into worm-like larvae. The larvae secrete a substance into the leaf tissue. The leaf then reacts to this secretion. It forms this gall, this tumorous swelling. The gall has a hard outer shell. This protects the larvae inside from other animals and, also, from the weather. Hence, the larvae have shelter. Inside the gall, spongy tissue is produced. This is food for the larvae. Thus, the larvae have all the food they need.

The larvae eat this food and reach mature size. Then, each changes into a wasp. The wasp makes a hole in the hard outer gall covering. Out it comes. Away it flies.

This is a very interesting thing, my friend. An animal - the wasp - asks the plant - the oak leaf - for food and shelter for its young.

The plant - the oak leaf - agrees and produces the Oak Apple - food and shelter - as requested.

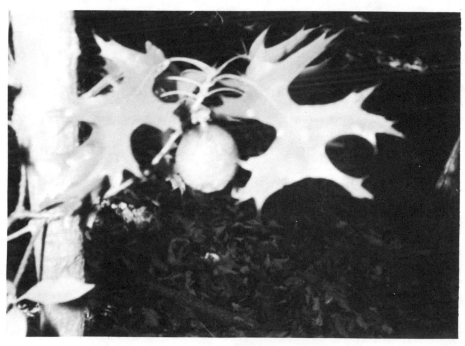

Look at the Box Turtle, my friend. Its life style is different from that of most turtles. Turtles, as a general rule, spend most of their lives in water. This Box Turtle prefers life on land.

The Box Turtle is quite an animal. Notice that its head, neck, four legs, and tail all project out of that box. The animal lives inside that box. As the animal grows, the box also grows. See those lines on the box covering. Those are growth lines. That orange and brown material showing growth lines is called keratin. This layer covers the bones that make up the box structure. Fingernails and claws of animals are also made of keratin.

One can tell the male turtles from the females. Just look at the color of the eyes. The males have some shade of red-colored eyes. Often their eyes are bright red in color. The female eye color is brown or brownish red.

Our Box Turtles stay here in our forest during the winter. From November until April, they live underground. They go underground when the weather gets colder. The turtles dig an underground spot with their front legs. They will stay there until spring. In April, the weather gets warmer. Out come the turtles!

It is at this time that the turtles mate. Then, the female finds a place to deposit its eggs. With its hind legs, it digs out a rounded space underground. Four or five eggs are usually deposited in this cavity.

Next, the turtle covers the narrow opening with dirt. It sweeps its hind feet backwards. This throws dirt over the spot. Then, the dirt is pressed down. It pushes its shell down on the dirt. It walks back and forth pressing down the dirt with its feet. Once the area is covered over, the female leaves. The eggs will now slowly change into small Box Turtles. This takes some time. At least two months are needed. Many times, it might take longer.

Our Box Turtles eat plant and animal food. Insects, earthworms, snails, and slugs are eaten by these turtles. They are also fond of mushrooms, berries, and fruit.

The Box Turtle has quite a shell. It pulls into the shell when a predator appears. It pulls in its head, neck, legs, and tail. Most animals flee to escape enemies. This turtle stays, but it shuts the doors. Inside, it is safe. Here, let me turn this turtle over.

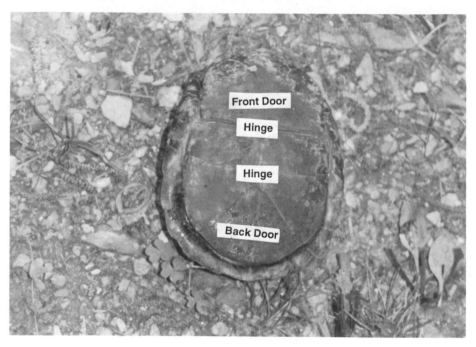

Front Door

Hinge

Hinge

Back Door

Look at the bottom of the turtle's box. Notice. There are two hinged doors. These fit securely into the top shell. When muscles open the front-hinged door, out come the head, neck, and two front legs. When the back-hinged door opens, out come the two hind legs and the tail. When danger threatens, the turtle pulls everything inside and closes the doors.

After a while, the turtle opens the front-hinged door a little bit. It looks around. If it looks safe to come out, the turtle will slowly emerge.

During the hot summers, the turtles go underground to escape the heat. They dig out temporary burrows. These are usually underneath logs or vegetation. When cooler weather returns, out come the Box Turtles. That, my friend, is our Box Turtle. It is quite an amazing animal.

Look at that woodland flower, my friend. That is a "Jack in the Pulpit" wild flower.

The leaf of the plant is a long stalk. There are three parts to the leaf. The flower is also on a long stalk. The pulpit around the flower is usually green.

The pulpit is often striped. A large canopy is over "Jack".

"Jack" is the tall spike - like f l o w e r standing in the pulpit under the canopy. The flower is not colored to draw many insects.

Instead, the flower uses an odor to attract flies to the plant. The pollinated flower produces mature berries. These are colored a bright red to attract animals to the plant.

My friend, we are very close to Ben's Branch, our forest stream. If we turn here, we will soon see the beavers' dam. There it is.

Two beavers made that dam. They cut down some rather tall trees. Then, they cut off the branches. They floated some tree parts down to the dam site. Some parts they pulled and floated. That is quite a dam. It is about four feet high. Look at the water backed up behind that dam. A large area of land was flooded when water was slowed down by the dam.

This flooding makes a small pond behind the dam. The beavers' home is constructed in that pond of water. It is a pile of branches so arranged as to make a central living space.   The beavers cover this living space with mud, thus making a floor.   There are several entrances to this beaver home.   Both entrances are under water. Here is a rough sketch of a beaver house.

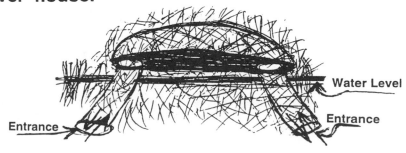

The beavers cut down trees to make their home and dam. Trees are always cut upstream from the dam. Branches are floated and pulled to the dam. The beavers can cut down rather large trees. Look at the size of this one.

That is a tree the beavers have just felled. Once the tree falls, the beaver cuts off branches. These branches are pulled into the water. The beaver swims toward the dam pulling the branches along. He will use the branches to make the dam stronger or to make the house bigger. Some of the branches will be stored for food.

Here is how a beaver cuts down a tree.

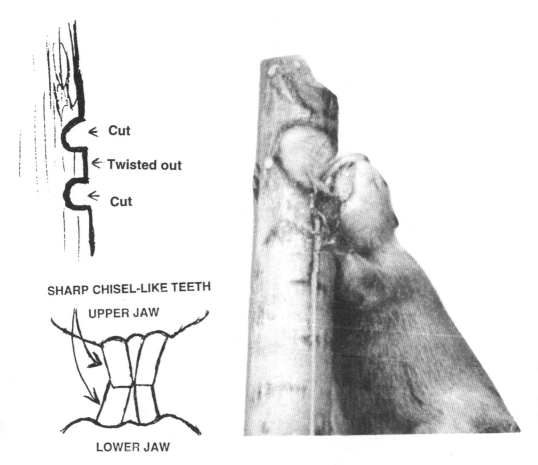

The beaver makes several bites into a tree with these strong teeth. Then, it repeats the process several inches above or several inches below these cuts. Next, it takes a firm grip on wood between these cuts. It twists out this chip. The chip drops to the ground. The beaver does this all around the trunk of the tree. Usually, the beaver does this while sitting. The beaver uses its tail as a prop.

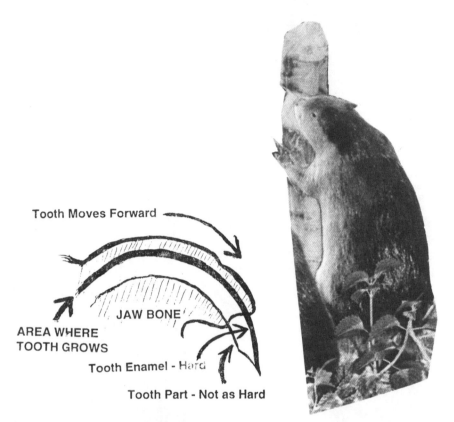

Tooth Moves Forward

AREA WHERE
TOOTH GROWS

JAW BONE

Tooth Enamel - Hard

Tooth Part - Not as Hard

The beaver's teeth are ideal for cutting wood. There are two cutting teeth in the upper jaw. Two teeth are in the lower jaw. The teeth are chisel-like. The upper set overlaps the lower set. The front surface of these teeth is covered with a thin orange layer. This is a layer of enamel. It is the hardest material in the animal. The rest of the tooth behind this thin layer is softer material. The back of the tooth wears down when biting a hard substance. This makes for a sharp cutting edge. As the tooth wears down, more tooth is made inside the jaw. The tooth is always growing.

Many animals have this tooth setup for cutting hard materials. Squirrels cut into acorns and hickory nuts with their front teeth. Mice and rats in the forest also cut up hard branches and nuts. But the beaver does it in grand style. It cuts down rather large trees.

Over here is another tree the beavers cut down. Notice all the chips of wood around that stump. Those chips are the wood the beavers cut away when they chiseled around that tree trunk.

That beaver is quite an engineer. Well, let's be off on our mail route.

Look at those beautiful Violet plants, my friend. Each of those flowers has five colored petals. That is characteristic of all Violets. The lower petal in the flower has lines on it. Those lines indicate to insects the way to sweet nectar. That lowest petal develops into a spur that points backwards. The nectar can be reached in the hollow area of the spur. One finds many Bumblebees visiting the Violets. The Violet plant blooms only a few months. During that time, it brings color and beauty to the forest areas.

CHAPTER SIX

LESTER - ON HIS MAIL ROUTE

Lester is walking through a field of Buttercups. There are many flowers in this moist area. The flowers shine, as it were. It looks like they have a coat of varnish on them. Buttercups are widely distributed in our forest. They brighten up clear areas in a forest.

Look over there, my friend. That is "Tootsie".

It is the favorite squirrel of the young "Yankoos". It is eating one of the acorns. Notice how it sits upright on its hind legs. The front feet are holding the acorn. The squirrel will cut a hole in the acorn. It has sharp teeth. It will cut away part of the acorn shell. Then, it will eat the soft nut inside.

When the acorns mature in our forest, the squirrels are busy. Acorns of the White Oak, Red Oak and the Black Oak are not identical in shape. The squirrel handles acorns from these trees differently.

Red Oak Acorn Black Oak Acorn White Oak Acorn

The squirrel will store acorns of the Red Oak and the Black Oak trees. It will eat the acorns of the White Oak tree first. Why? Well, acorns of the White Oak sprout early. Acorns of the Red Oak and the Black Oak sprout later. Squirrels are not too interested in sprouted acorns. They cannot easily digest them. So, the squirrel will eat the White Oak acorns first. Soon, the White Oak acorns will begin sprouting. Then, the squirrel starts to eat the Red Oak and Black Oak acorns. The squirrel eats all of these kinds of acorns. But it does not eat them all at the same time. It eats the White Oak first. It saves the ones which store well for later. It eats the White Oak acorns before they spoil. The others last for some time. It eats them later when the White Oak acorns sprout.

Squirrels live mostly in the trees. They glide from one tree to another. They leap from one branch to another. They have long hind legs and can jump some distance. When it jumps from one tree to another, it uses its long bushy tail as a rudder.

Many squirrels gather a lot of leaves and twigs. These are placed in a mass in the fork of a tree high above the ground. They use this as a shelter. The squirrels stay with us all year.

The squirrel has relatively long toes and claws for climbing. The squirrel comes down a tree, head first.

Very few animals descend a tree, head first. Most animals come down a tree, tail first. They back down a tree trunk. The squirrel has a special setup. It can swivel the ankle. By turning the ankle, it can point the claws backward. This specialized ankle allows the squirrel to climb head first in both directions. It goes head first down the tree trunk.

The normal position of the ankle points the claws forward. This is the position of the ankle and claws going up the tree.

Going Up a Tree Trunk

Now, suppose that was the claws' position coming head first down the tree. The claws would not be able to hold the animal to the tree. The animal would fall forward. Most animals back down a tree because they cannot swivel their ankles like a squirrel does.

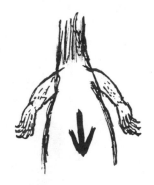

Coming Down a Tree Trunk

In coming down the trunk, it swivels its ankles. It twists the ankles around so that the claws point backward. Now, the claws can hold the animal to the trunk as it descends.

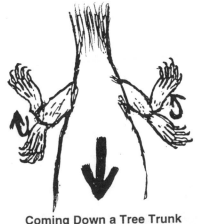

Coming Down a Tree Trunk

Squirrels are active early in the morning. For several hours after sunrise, they are active. Then, one does not see them until the middle of the afternoon. During the summer, the squirrels eat nuts, buds, fruits, berries, flowers, mushrooms, grapes, and wild cherries.

See, they even hide acorns in old tree stumps. Squirrels have large, protruding eyes. This is characteristic of animals which are active during the day. They have good binocular and lateral vision. This good vision helps squirrels stay alive. Let's be on our way, my friend.

Look at that lichen on the tree trunk, my friend.

That lichen is not a plant - it is two plants. One part of the lichen is a fungus. It is a simple thread-like plant. It adheres to the bark. It forms a tough framework holding the second plant. The second plant is an alga.

Algae can be either single cells or cell groups. These two plants make a lichen. The fungus supplies proper shelter for the algae. It also supplies water and mineral food. The alga, being green, produces organic food units. These units are used to make more fungi threads. The units also make more algae plants. This partnership is called a lichen.

Up ahead is Old Zeb's hut. He is there. He sees us. Hi, Zeb! I brought a friend along, today. He is learning about the forest and the Yankoos. Hello, friend. Glad to meet you. Look what I have in my hands. It is a fish. I attached some horns to the front of the fish. Then, I found some young Yankoos. Look what I have, I said, a deep sea fish with some horns on it. They just laughed. They said, Zeb, you are trying to fool us again. You put those horns on that fish. I have a hard time fooling them, but I keep trying. I do believe they enjoy my pranks.

Zeb, tell our friend what you do. Oh, gladly, Lester. I grow vegetables for the forest Yankoos. You can see my garden. There are rows and rows of vegetables.

When I am not tending my garden, I watch forest insects. The forest has many interesting insects, for example, that Luna Moth on the tree over there. I have been watching it. It will fly away when it gets dark.

See that patch of Black-eyed Susans over there.

Those flowers brighten up our forest. They also have many insects. The flowers are very beautiful. Each flower has some twenty to forty orange-yellow petals. They point, as it were, to the center. In the middle is a hill-shaped area of dark brown flowers. These dark brown flowers have the nectar and the pollen the insects seek. The colored petals reflect some of the sun's rays. The reflected rays lead bees to the flowers in the center. Many insects can be found on those Black-eyed Susan flowers. Bees, flies, grasshoppers, and even spiders drop in for food.

Let's look closely at that patch of flowers. Perhaps, we can find a Crab Spider on one of those flowers.

Yes, there is one! It is white in color. It is easy to spot. Often, a spider is the color of those petals, orange-yellow. Notice it has long pointed legs. They are spread wide apart. An insect will settle down on that flower. Immediately, those legs will grab it. The spider injects a poison into the insect. The spider then sucks the body fluids from the insect.

The insect body will be drained of all liquids. Then, the spider casts away the dry carcass. Here is a drawing of a Crab Spider, my friend. It looks like a crab. It moves like a crab. It moves fast. It can go forward, backward, or even sideways. This is the way the crabs move. So, this spider

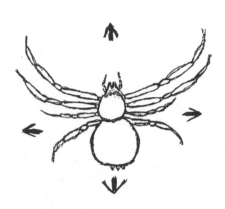

gets its name honestly. It is a spider, very much like a crab - hence, a Crab Spider.   Look down there!

There is a bee on a Black-eyed Susan. If you look closely, you can see the grasshopper on another Black-eyed Susan in that patch of flowers.

Well, my friend, we are nearing the end of my mail route. We will drop by to say hello to Sam. Sam is our Yankoo Elder. I see him over there. He is standing in front of his hut.

Hi, Sam! Hi, Lester! I see you have a friend with you. Yes, Sam, he has traveled many-a-day with me. Sam, tell our friend what you do in the forest. Gladly, will I do that, Lester. I help any Yankoo that needs help. That is my main job. It just seems right that I spend my time helping others. That is one good reason why I exist.

Here I hold the book, the Yankoo Law. It is a small book. The entire law is on one page. It reads: Yankoos-love one another. They do this. Yet, now and then, a problem does occur. As Elder, I meet with these Yankoos. I open the book. I read the sentence that resolves most problems.

Each Yankoo knows what must be done. It is because of this law that our Yankoos are such a happy bunch. Thank you, Sam. I am sure my friend now realizes why our Yankoos are so happy in our forest. My friend, I must now go back to the main Yankoo Post Office. Olaf, the postmaster, will be waiting for me.

My friend, I must leave you, now. All the Yankoos hope that you have enjoyed your travel through our forest. If so, tell your friends about us. Perhaps, they would also enjoy traveling through our forest.

In the meantime, I know that you would enjoy a visit with our Yankoo relatives living in the desert. Roscoe, the Yankoo Desert Ranger, will amaze you with stories about desert plants and animals. They manage to live interesting lives in that hot and dry desert. Read about them in the Yankoo Series of Books on the Desert. Now, all the Oak-Hickory Forest Yankoos say: "GOODBYE, MY FRIEND."

TRACKING IT DOWN

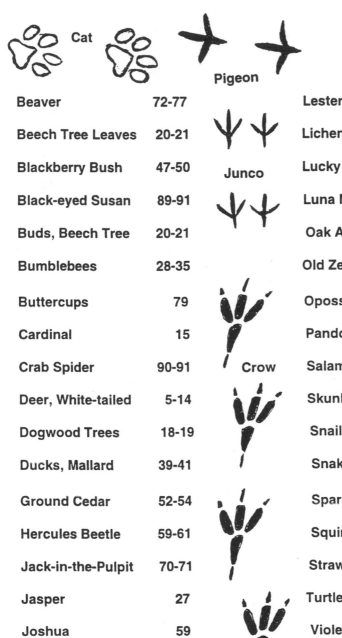

Pigeon

Junco

Crow

  Rabbit

AMERICAN ELVES - THE YANKOOS

The Yankoos and the Oak-Hickory Forest Ecology

This is the fifth and final book in this series on the forest. These books, presenting the wonders of nature in a forest, make ideal gifts for children. All five books of the series are now available for purchase.

Book One: Illustrated, 64 pages
             Soft cover, 6x9.....................$7.95

Book Two: Illustrated, 96 pages
             Soft cover, 6x9.....................$7.95

Book Three: Illustrated, 96 pages
             Soft cover, 6x9.....................$7.95

Book Four: Illustrated, 96 pages
             Soft cover, 6x9...............$7.95

Book Five: Illustrated, 96 pages
             Soft cover, 6x9...............$7.95

Shipping and handling:.........$2.50
Allow two weeks for U. S. Postal Delivery-Book Rate

COMPLETE SERIES OF FIVE BOOKS.......$35.00 pp.

Make checks payable to:
Yankoo Publishing Co.
10616 W. Cameo Dr.
Sun City, AZ 85351-2708